Eternal Flame
+15 Smash Hits

D0417493

This publication is not authorised for
sale in the United States of America and / or Canada

Wise Publications
London / New York / Paris / Sydney/ Copenhagen / Madrid / Tokyo

Exclusive Distributors:
Music Sales Limited
8/9 Frith Street, London W1D 3JB, England.
Music Sales Pty Limited
120 Rothschild Avenue, Rosebery, NSW 2018, Australia.

Order No. AM972290
ISBN 0-7119-9128-6
This book © Copyright 2001 by Wise Publications.

Unauthorised reproduction of any part of this publication by
any means including photocopying is an infringement of copyright.

Music arranged by Derek Jones.
Music processed by Paul Ewers Music Design.
Cover photographs courtesy of London Features International.
Printed in Great Britain by Printwise (Haverhill) Limited, Suffolk

Your Guarantee of Quality
As publishers, we strive to produce every book to the highest commercial standards.
The music has been freshly engraved and the book has been carefully designed to minimise
awkward page turns and to make playing from it a real pleasure.
Throughout, the printing and binding have been planned to ensure a sturdy,
attractive publication which should give years of enjoyment.
If your copy fails to meet our high standards, please inform us and we will gladly replace it.

Music Sales' complete catalogue describes thousands of titles and is available in
full colour sections by subject, direct from Music Sales Limited.
Please state your areas of interest and send a cheque/postal order for £1.50 for postage to:
Music Sales Limited, Newmarket Road, Bury St. Edmunds, Suffolk IP33 3YB, England.

www.musicsales.com

Eternal Flame

Words & Music by Billy Steinberg, Tom Kelly & Susanna Hoffs

© Copyright 1988 & 1989 Billy Steinberg Music/Sony/ATV Tunes LLC/Bangophile Music, USA.
Sony/ATV Music Publishing (UK) Limited, 10 Great Marlborough Street, London W1 (66.67%)/Copyright Control (33.33%).
All Rights Reserved. International Copyright Secured.

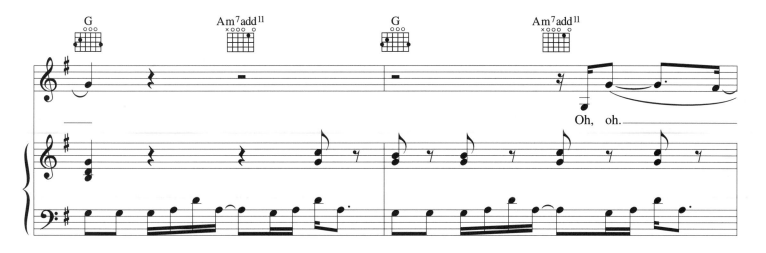

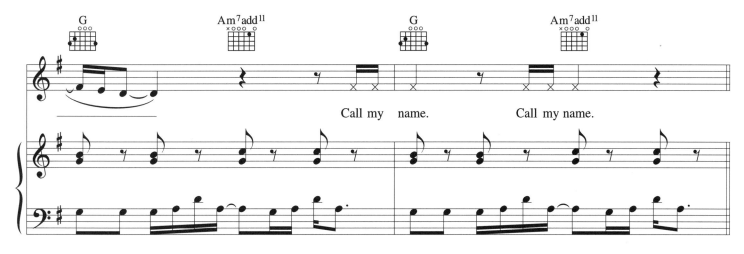

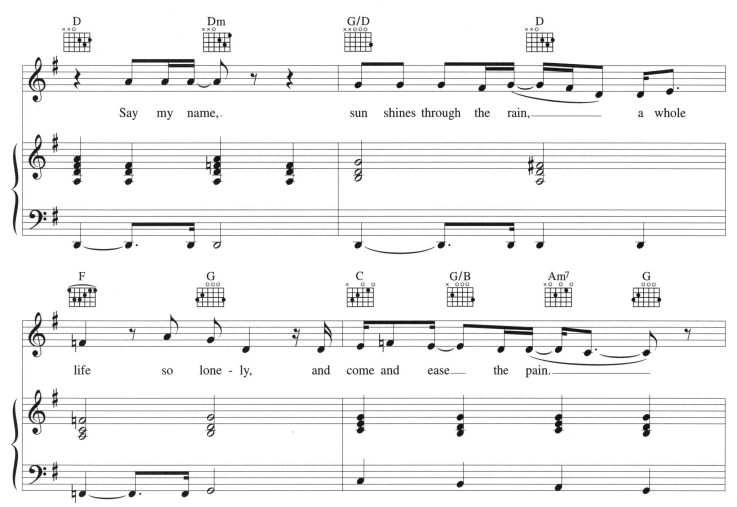

Don't Stop Movin'

Words & Music by Simon Ellis, Sheppard Solomon & S Club 7

© Copyright 2001 19 Music Limited/BMG Music Publishing Limited,
Bedford House, 69-79 Fulham High Street, London SW6 (37.5%)/
Rondor Music (London) Limited, 10a Parsons Green, London SW6 (37.5%)/
Universal Music Publishing Limited, 77 Fulham Palace Road, London W6 (25%).
All Rights Reserved. International Copyright Secured.

stop mov-in', find your own way to it. Lis - ten to the mu-sic. tak-

- ing you to pla - ces that you've nev - er been be-fore, ba - by now.

Don't stop mov-in' to the

fun - ky, fun - ky beat. Don't stop mov - in' to the fun - ky, fun - ky beat.

Don't stop mov-in' to the fun-ky, fun-ky beat. Don't stop mov-in' to the

fun - ky, fun - ky beat. Yeah, oh come on! Don't stop mov-in' to the

fun - ky, fun - ky beat. Don't stop mov-in' to the fun-ky, fun - ky beat.

For-get a-bout your fears— to - night,— lis - ten to your heart,let's just touch— the sky.—

No need— to rea - son— why.— Just lis-ten to the sound and it makes— you come a - live.— Don't

Don't stop mov-in' to the fun-ky, fun-ky beat. Don't stop mov-in' to the

fun - ky, fun - ky beat. Don't stop mov-in' to the

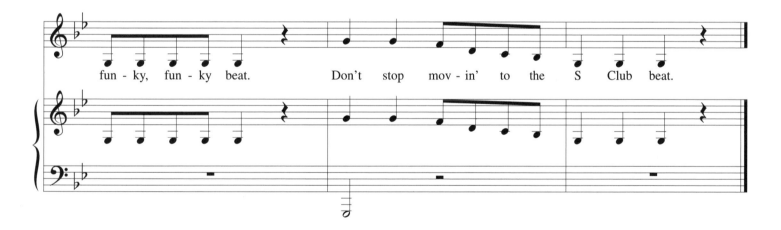

fun - ky, fun - ky beat. Don't stop mov-in' to the S Club beat.

Verse 3:
You can touch the moment almost feel it in the air
Don't know where we're goin' baby we don't even care
Ain't no mystery, just use your imagination
Let it take you there
Just go with the magic baby
I can see it there in your eyes
Let it flow, stop the waiting, right here on the dance floor
Is where you gotta let it go.

Don't stop movin' can you feel the music *etc.*

Eternity

Words & Music by Robbie Williams & Guy Chambers

1. Close your eyes so you don't feel them,
(Verse 2 see block lyric)

they don't need to see you cry. I can pro-mise I will

© Copyright 2001 BMG Music Publishing Limited, Bedford House, 69-79 Fulham High Street, London SW6 (50%)/
EMI Music Publishing Limited, 127 Charing Cross Road, London WC2 (50%).
All Rights Reserved. International Copyright Secured.

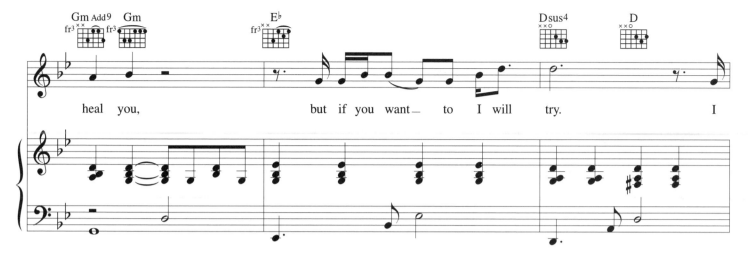

heal you, but if you want— to I will try. I

sing this sum-mer se - re - nade,_ the past is done, we've been_ be-trayed

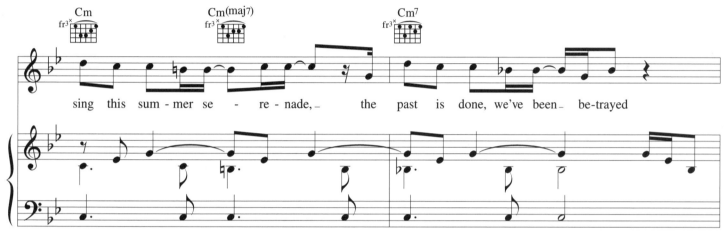

it's true._ Some - one said the truth_ will out_ and

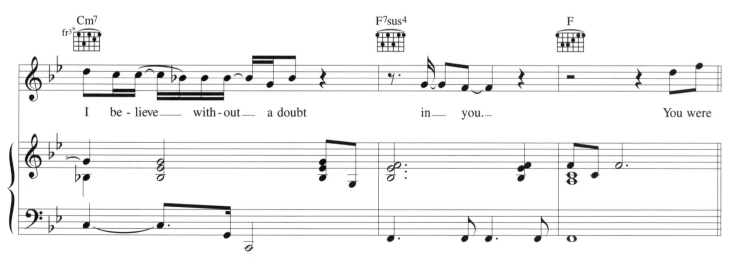

I be - lieve_ with-out_ a doubt in_ you._ You were

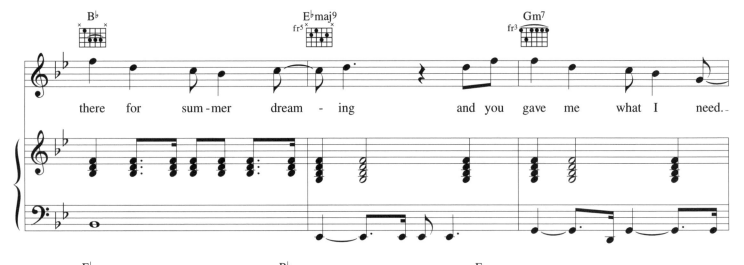

there for sum-mer dream-ing and you gave me what I need.__

__ And I hope you'll find your free - dom __ for e-ter-ni-ty.__

1.

__ For e-ter - ni-ty.

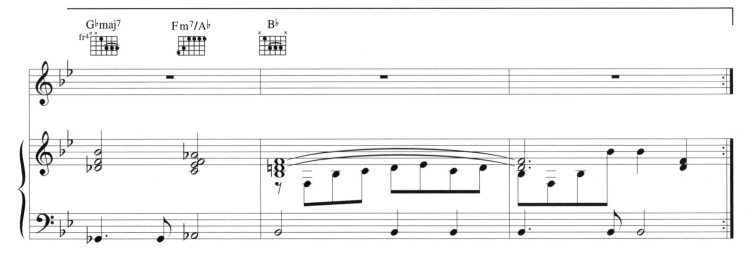

-ty. (Ah. _____)

(8va) _ _ _ _ For e - ter - ni - ty. ___ (Ah. _____)

I sing this sum-mer se - re - nade, _ the past is done, we've been be-trayed

it's true. _ Youth is wast-ed on _ the young _ be-

Verse 2:

Yesterday when you were walking
We talked about your Mum and Dad
What they did that made you happy
What they did that made you sad
We sat and watched the sun go down
Picked a star before we lost the moon
Youth is wasted on the young
Before you know, it's come and gone too soon.

You were there for summer dreaming *etc.*

Have A Nice Day

Words & Music by Kelly Jones

© Copyright 2001 Stereophonics Music Limited/
Universal Music Publishing Limited, 77 Fulham Palace Road, London W6.
All Rights Reserved. International Copyright Secured.

re-mem-ber what time.— Got the wait-ing cab, stopped at the red light.

Add-ress we're sure of, but it's turned out just right.

2. It start-ed straight off "Com - ing here is hell." That's his first words,
(Verses 3 & 4 see block lyrics)

we asked   what he   meant.—   He said "And where ya from?"   We told him our   lot,

"Ya take a ho-li-day,   is this   what   you   want?"

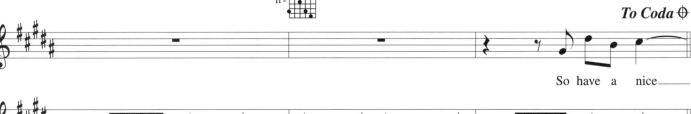

To Coda ⊕

So have a nice———

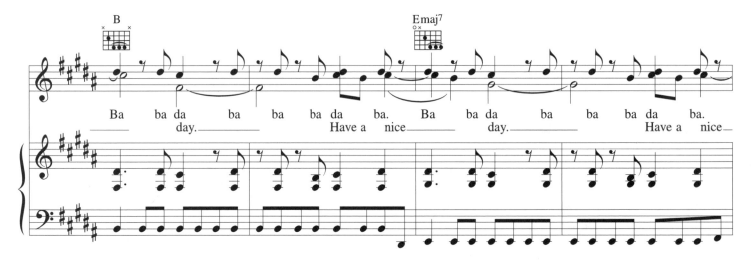

Ba   ba da   ba   ba   ba da   ba.   Ba   ba da   ba   ba   ba da   ba.
        day.———   Have a nice———   day.   Have a nice

Ba ba da ba ba ba da ba. Ba ba da ba ba ba da ba.
day. Have a nice day.

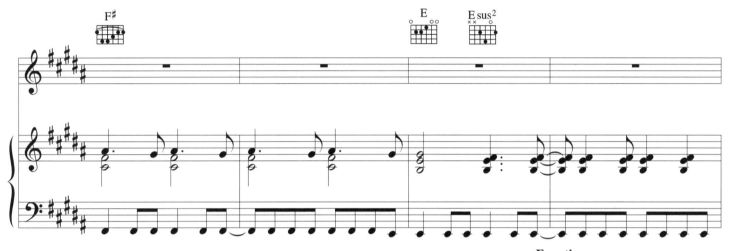

Free time

Oh.

a tempo

D.%. al Coda

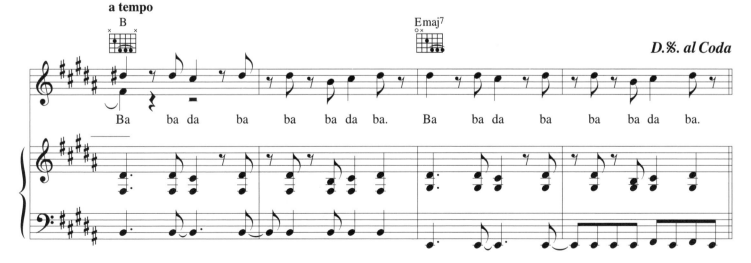

Ba ba da ba ba ba da ba. Ba ba da ba ba ba da ba.

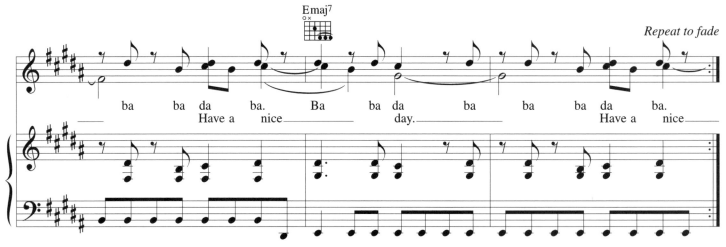

Verse 3:

Lie around all day
Have a drink to chase
Yourself and tourists, yeah
That's what I hate
He said "We're going wrong
We've all become the same
We dress the same ways
Only our accents change."

So have a nice day *etc.*

Verse 4:

Swim in the ocean
That be my dish
I drive around all day
And kill processed fish
It's all money gum
No artists any more
You're only in it now
To make more, more, more.

So have a nice day *etc.*

It's Raining Men

Words & Music by Paul Jabara & Paul Shaffer

© Copyright 1983 Postvalda Music/EMI Sosaha Music Incorporated/Jonathan Three Music Company, USA.
Warner Chappell Music Limited, Griffin House, 161 Hammersmith Road, London W6 (50%)/
EMI Songs Limited, 127 Charing Cross Road, London WC2 (26.87%)/
Sony/ATV Music Publishing (UK) Limited, 10 Great Marlborough Street, London W1 (23.13%).
All Rights Reserved. International Copyright Secured.

time,   just a - bout half - past ten,   for the

first time in his - to - ry it's gon - na start rain - ing men,

1.

(Start rain - ing men)   It's rain - ing men,   hal - le - lu -

- jah! It's rain - ing men, A - men! It's rain - ing men,

ab - so - lute - ly soak - ing wet!__ It's rain - ing men,

hal - le - lu - jah! It's rain - ing men,__ ev - 'ry spe -

- ci - men!__ Tall, blonde, dark and lean.__

Rough and tough__ and strong__ and mean._____

God bless Moth-er Na - ture, she's a sin - gle wo-

- man too.— She took— off to hea - ven

and she did what she had to do. She taught— ev - 'ry an-

- gel to re - ar - range the sky— so that

35

Juxtapozed With U

Words & Music by Gruff Rhys, Dafydd Ieuan,
Guto Pryce, Huw Bunford & Cian Ciarán

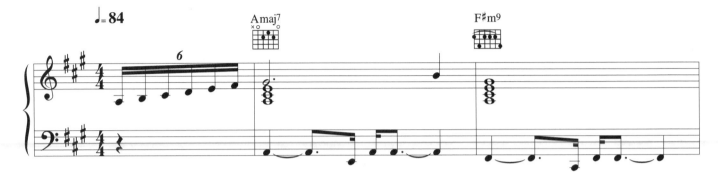

1. It's ea - sy when you know how, to get a - long with - out biff!_ bang! pow!_
(Verse 2 see block lyric)

© Copyright 2001 Universal Music Publishing Limited, 77 Fulham Palace Road, London W6.
All Rights Reserved. International Copyright Secured.

And if I see you're fed— up I'll stop and give you a leg— up.

Ov - er priced un-real— es-tate,— sur - real— es-tate. The high-est price they've hit—

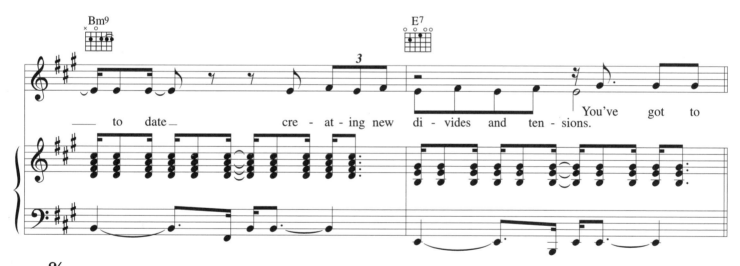

— to date — cre - at - ing new di - vides and ten - sions. You've got to

to - ler-ate— all those peo-ple that you hate.. I'm not in love— with you,— but I won't

Verse 2:
This is a tale of two situations
Mutual appreciation
Away from narrow pre-conception
Avoiding conflict, hypertension
Non-phobic word aerobic
This was my domain till someone stole my name.

You've got to tolerate *etc.*

A Little Respect

Words & Music by Vince Clarke & Andy Bell

1. I tried to dis - cov - er ___
(Verse 2 see block lyric)
a lit - tle some-thing to make ___ me sweet - er.

Oh, ba - by re - frain ___

© Copyright 1988 Musical Moments Limited/Minotaur Music Limited/
Sony/ATV Music Publishing (UK) Limited, 10 Great Marlborough Street, London W1.
All Rights Reserved. International Copyright Secured.

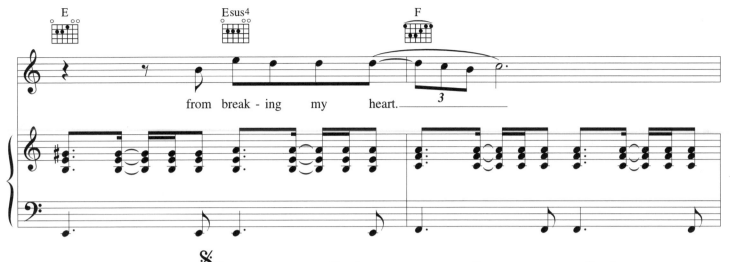

from break - ing my heart.

I'm so — in love — with you, — I'll be — for - ev -

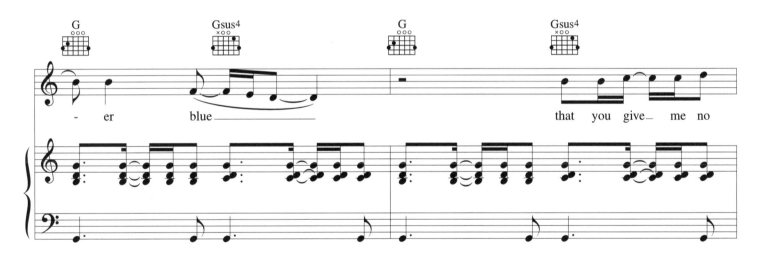

- er blue _____ that you give — me no

rea - son, _____ you know you're mak - ing me work so — hard —

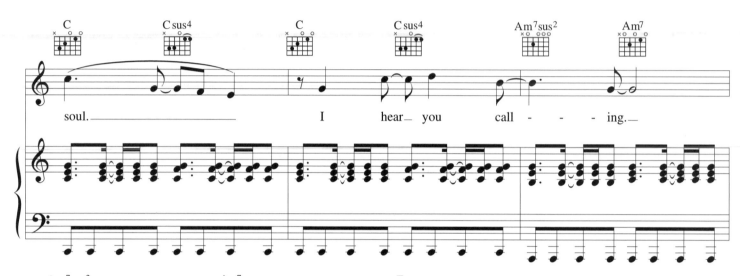

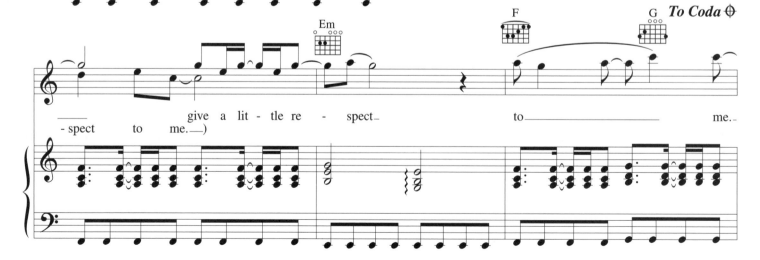

2. And if— I should fal -

D.%. al Coda

I'm so— in love—

Coda

— I hear— you call - - ing.—

Verse 2 :
And if I should falter
Would you open your arms out to me
We can make love not war
And live with peace in our hearts
I'm so in love with you
I'll be forever blue
What religion or reason
Could drive a man to forsake his lover
Don't you tell me no, don't you tell me no
Don't you tell me no, don't you tell me no.

So, I hear you calling *etc.*

Made For Lovin' You

Words & Music by Anastacia, Sam Watters & Louis Biancaniello

© Copyright 2000 Breakthrough Creations/S.M.Y. Publishing/Sony/ATV Tunes LLC/Poho Productions, USA.
Sony/ATV Music Publishing (UK) Limited, 10 Great Marlborough Street, London W1 (66.67%)/
Universal Music Publishing Limited, 77 Fulham Palace Road, London W6 (33.33%).
All Rights Reserved. International Copyright Secured.

don't keep me wait-ing on that out-side love._____ Can't stop it if you

want-ed to___ 'cause I was made for lov-in' you. Yeah,__ yeah.

It's time that you let me know,__ ba-by._____ I ain't go-ing, I

ain't gon-na play__ your games.__ Can't face a-no-ther day._____ There's

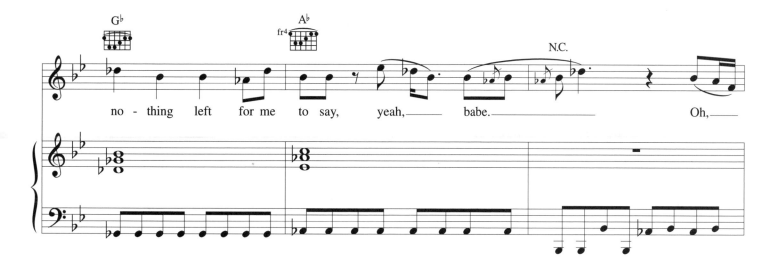

no - thing left for me to say, yeah, _____ babe. _____ Oh, _____

oh, _____ oh, _____ yeah, _____ yeah, _____ yeah, _____ yeah, _____ yeah, yeah.

D.%. Repeat chorus to fade

Verse 2:
I guess I thought it was a dream
Locked up in a mystery
Can't guess all what was meant to be
My soul just keeps on telling me, yeah, yeah
'Cause I can't take this for another day
I've thought of us a hundred different ways
And I'd do anything for you
'Cause you are made for lovin' me
And me for lovin' you.

Now I wanna take you higher *etc.*

Out Of Reach

Words & Music by Gabrielle & Jonathan Shorten

© Copyright 2001 Perfect Songs Limited, The Blue Building, 42-46 St. Luke's Mews, London W11 (50%)/
Universal Music Publishing Limited, 77 Fulham Palace Road, London W6 (50%).
All Rights Reserved. International Copyright Secured.

and now I feel like a fool.

So con - fused. my heart's bruised.

Was I ev - er loved by you? Out of reach,

so far. I nev - er had your heart.

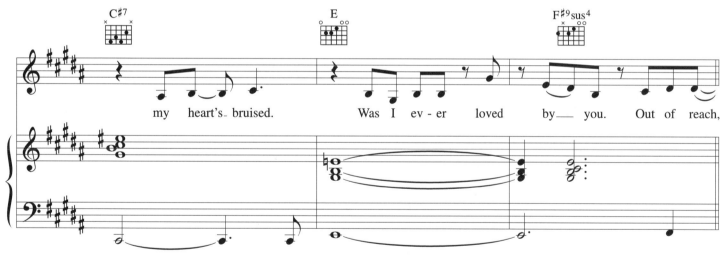

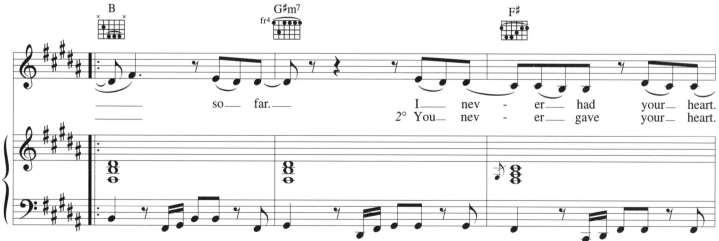

Verse 2:
Catch myself from despair
I could drown if I stay here
Keeping busy every day
I know I will be O.K.
But I was so confused
My heart's bruised
Was I ever loved by you?

Out of reach *etc.*

Sing

Words & Music by Fran Healy

1. Ba-by, you've been go-in' so cra-zy, late-
(Verse 2 see block lyric)
-ly no-thin' seems to be go-in' right. So

© Copyright 2001 Sony/ATV Music Publishing (UK) Limited, 10 Great Marlborough Street, London W1.
All Rights Reserved. International Copyright Secured.

a - lone, oh, why d'ya have to get so a-lone? You're

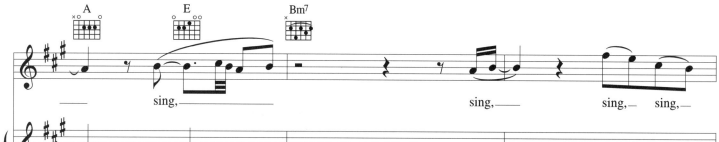

sore, you've been wait - in' in the sun too long. But if you sing,

sing, sing, sing, sing,

sing, for the love you bring won't mean a thing

un-less you sing,— sing,— sing,— sing.———— 2. Cold—

Ooh.————————————

Oh,—— oh,———— oh.

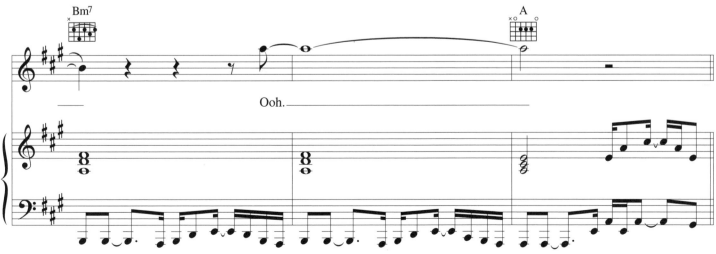

Ooh.————————————

3. Ba - by, there's some-thing go - in' wrong to - day,

but I say no-thing, no - thing, no - thing, no-thing, no-thing,

no-thing, no-thing, no-thing, no-thing, no-thing. So na, na, na, na, now if you sing,

sing, sing, sing,

Verse 2:
Colder, crying over your shoulder
Hold her, tell her everything's gonna be fine
Surely you've been going to hurry
Hurry, 'cos no-one's gonna be stopped.

Not if you sing *etc.*

Sail Away

Words & Music by David Gray

Sail a-way— with me, ho-ney, I put my heart— in your hands.

Sail a-way— with me ho-ney now,— now,— now.—

© Copyright 1998 Chrysalis Music Limited, The Chrysalis Building, Bramley Road, London W10.
All Rights Reserved. International Copyright Secured.

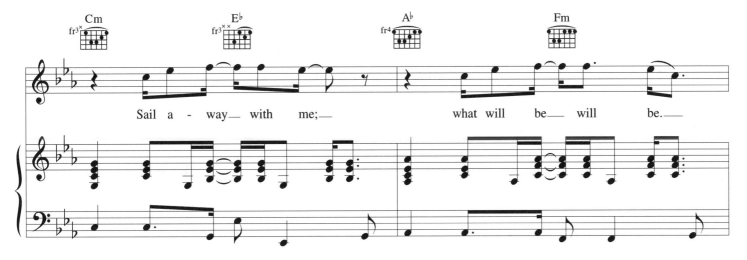

Sail a - way— with me;— what will be— will be.—

I wan-na hold you— now,— now,— now.—

— Cra - zy skies— all wild— a - bove— me now,—

win - ter howl - ing at my face;—

and ev - 'ry - thing___ I held___ so dear___

dis - ap - peared___ with - out a trace.___

1. Though all the times___ I tast - ed love,___
(Verse 2 see block lyric)

nev - er knew___ quite___ what I had.

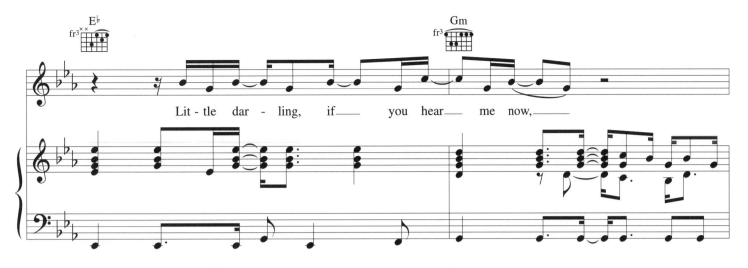

Lit - tle dar - ling, if___ you hear___ me now,___

nev - er need-ed you so bad;___

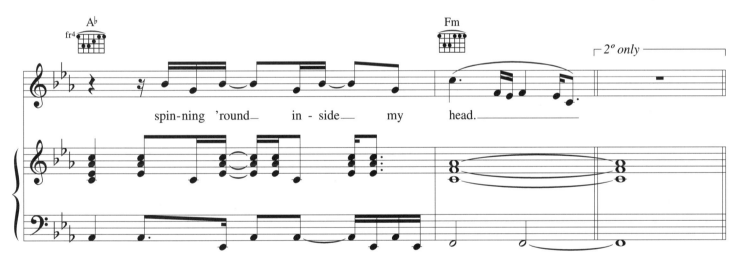

spin-ning 'round___ in - side___ my head.___

┌─ *2° only* ─┐

Sail a - way___ with me, ho-ney, I put my heart___ in your hands.

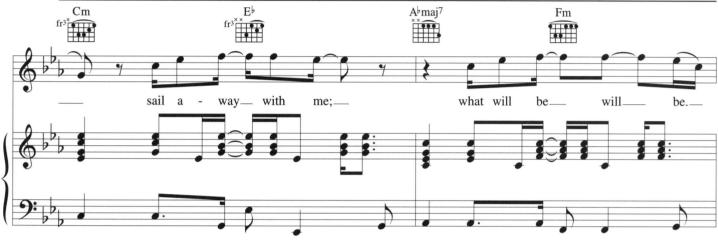

Verse 2:
I've been talking drunken gibberish
Falling in and out of bars
Trying to get some explanation here
For the way some people are.
How did it ever come so far?

Chorus 5:
Sail away with me, honey
I put my heart in your hands.
It break me up if you put me down, woh…
Sail away with me; what will be will be.
I wanna hold you now, now, now.

Chorus 6 & 7:
(Whistle)

Sometimes

Words & Music by Tim Wheeler

1. Can't sleep in the ci-ty you're far a-way,— ci-gar-

© Copyright 2001 Universal/Island Music Limited, 77 Fulham Palace Road, London W6.
All Rights Reserved. International Copyright Secured.

some - times. Oh, some - times,— some - times.

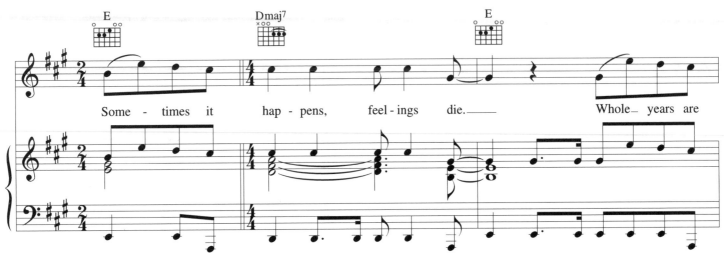

Some - times it hap - pens, feel - ings die.— Whole— years are

lost in the blink of an eye.— We once had it all, but e - vents con - spired.

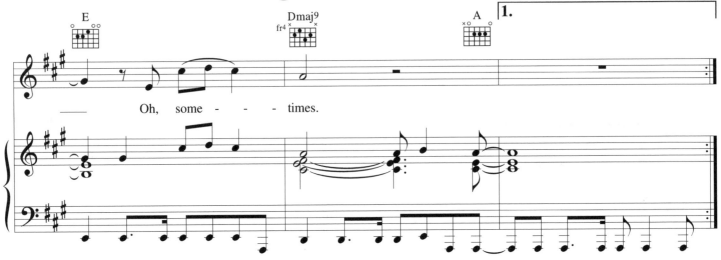

— Oh, some - - times.

2.

And now that it is ov - er and it is through,— it gets me ev - 'ry -

time I think of——— you.——— And some - times it hap - pens, feel - ings die.—

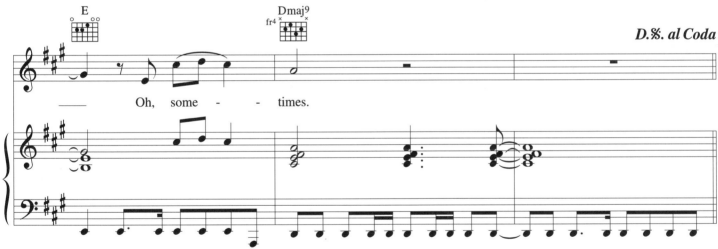

D.%. al Coda

——— Oh, some - — - times.

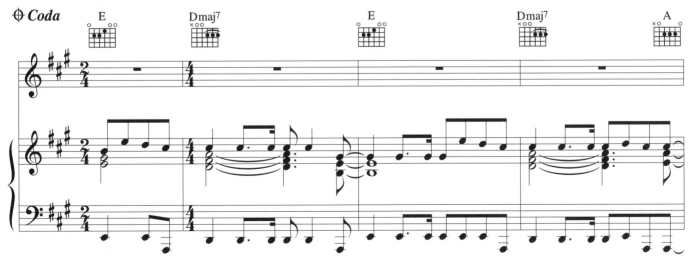

✠ Coda

-cline in my star sign.___ Sea - son - al ad - just - ments, stars re - al - ign.___

Some - thing it hap - pens, feel - ings die.___ Oh, some - -

- times, some - - - times.

Verse 3:
Good morning sweet thing
You're safe in my hands
I am no saint
But I understand
Oh, sometimes, sometimes
Oh, sometimes, sometimes.

Sometime it happens etc.

Verse 4:
I miss your warm skin
Beside me at night
And I miss your flesh
In the dawn light
Oh, sometimes, sometimes
Oh, sometimes, sometimes.

Stone By Stone

**Words & Music by Cerys Matthews, Mark Roberts,
Aled Richards, Paul Jones & Owen Powell**

1. You al-ways hear the shouts from my ba-tal-li-on
(Verse 2 see block lyric)

© Copyright 2001 Sony/ATV Music Publishing (UK) Limited, 10 Great Marlborough Street, London W1.
All Rights Reserved. International Copyright Secured.

stone by___ stone___ and how___

With more and more you know it won't take__ long,__ where it burns

1.
or - ange__ let__ it burn__ gold.___ gold.

2.
___ gold.___

Repeat to fade

Verse 2:
I wouldn't like to learn a lesson every day
Good times, bad times just a price to pay
But given half a chance of turning back the tide
I'd stay at home and keep my boys in line.

On common ground *etc.*

Survivor

Words & Music by Beyoncé Knowles,
Anthony Dent & Matthew Knowles

1. Now that you're

out-ta my life, I'm so much better. You thought that I'd be weak with-out_ you, but I'm stronger. You thought that I'd be
(Verse 2 see block lyric)

© Copyright 2001 Beyoncé Publishing/Sony/ATV Tunes LLC/Hitco South/Chase Muzic Incorporated/Music Of Windswept, USA.
Windswept Music (London) Limited, Hope House, 40 St. Peter's Road, London W6 (50%)/
Sony/ATV Music Publishing (UK) Limited, 10 Great Marlborough Street, London W1 (47%)/Copyright Control (3%).
All Rights Reserved. International Copyright Secured.

broke without — you, but I'm richer. You thought that I'd be sad without — you, I laugh harder. Thought I wouldn't

grow without — you, now I'm wiser. Thought that I'd be helpless with-out you, but I'm smarter, You thought that I'd be

stressed with-out — you, but I'm chill-in'. You thought I would-n't sell with-out — you, sold nine million. I'm a sur-

-vi - vor, I'm not gon' give up. I'm not gon' stop, (what) I'm gon' work hard - er. I'm a sur-

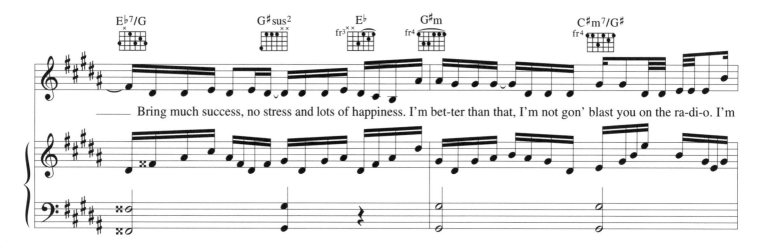

Bring much success, no stress and lots of happiness. I'm bet-ter than that, I'm not gon' blast you on the ra-di-o. I'm

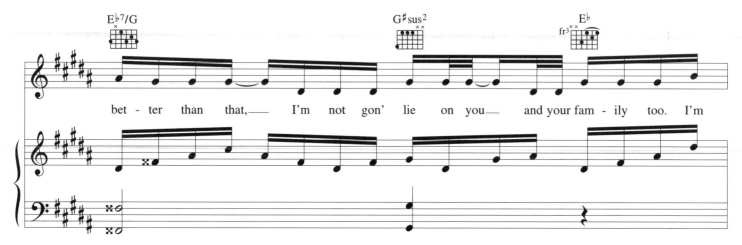

bet - ter than that,___ I'm not gon' lie on you___ and your fam - ily too. I'm

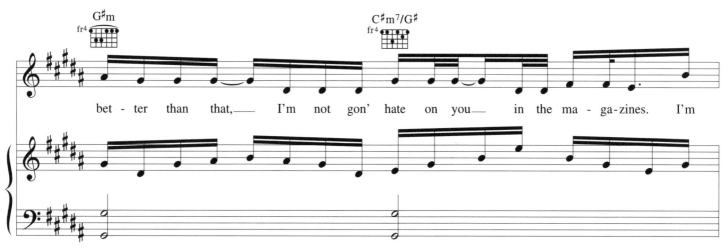

bet - ter than that,___ I'm not gon' hate on you___ in the ma - ga - zines. I'm

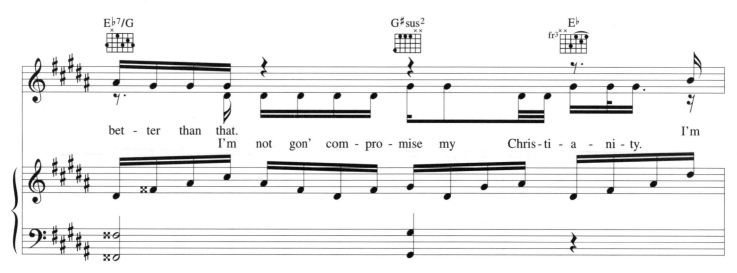

bet - ter than that.

I'm not gon' com - pro - mise my Chris - ti - a - ni - ty.

I'm

bet - ter than that. You know I'm not gon' diss you on the in - ter - net,—

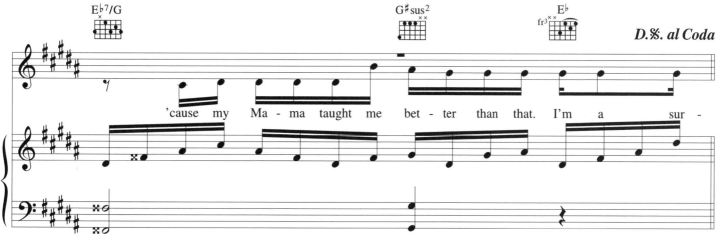

'cause my Ma - ma taught me bet - ter than that. I'm a sur -

D.%. al Coda

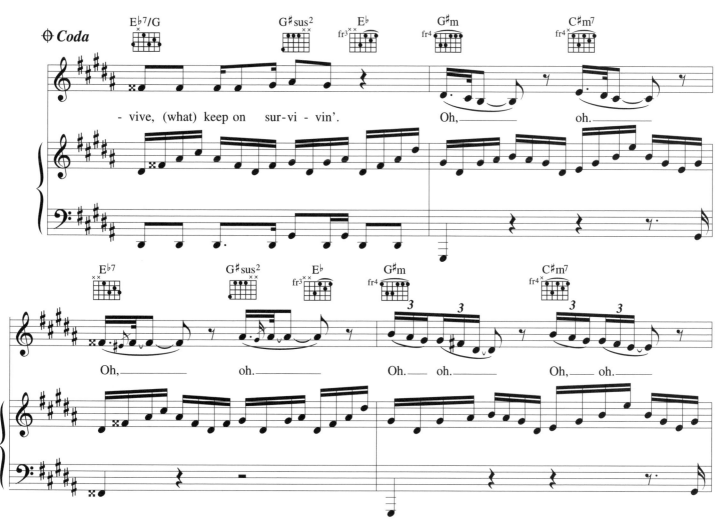

✛ *Coda*

- vive, (what) keep on sur - vi - vin'. Oh,_____ oh._____

Oh,_____ oh. Oh.— oh._____ Oh,_____ oh._____

Verse 2:
Thought I couldn't breathe without you, I'm inhalin'
Thought I couldn't see without you, perfect vision
Thought I couldn't last without you, but I'm lastin'
Thought that I would die without you, but I'm livin'
Thought that I would fail without you, but I'm on top
Thought that it would be over by now, but it won't stop
Thought that I would self-destruct, but I'm still here
Even in my years to come, I'm still gonna be here.

I'm a survivor *etc.*

The Way To Your Love

Words & Music by Mikkel SE, Hallgeir Rustan & Tor Erik Hermansen

© Copyright 2001 EMI Music Publishing Limited, 127 Charing Cross Road, London WC2 (66.67%)/
Sony/ATV Music Publishing (UK) Limited, 10 Great Marlborough Street, London W1 (33.33%).
All Rights Reserved. International Copyright Secured.

hold you and nev - er let go.___ Oh no.___ For as long as we're giv - ing and we

nev - er pre - tend,___ I be - lieve in the fu - ture un - told.___ We'll be

strong - er to - geth - er than we would be a - part.___ I can

feel you in - side___ my heart.___ Ev - 'ry

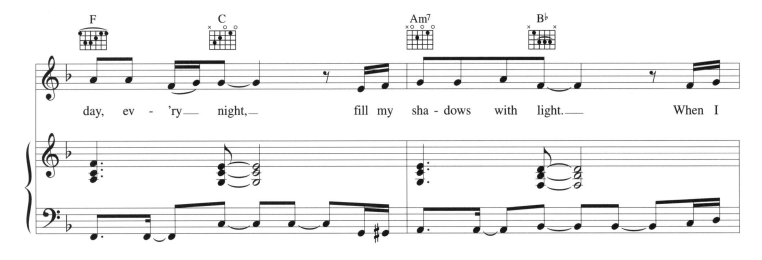

day, ev - 'ry— night,— fill my sha - dows with light.— When I

feel all a - lone— your heart is my home.— Ev - 'ry

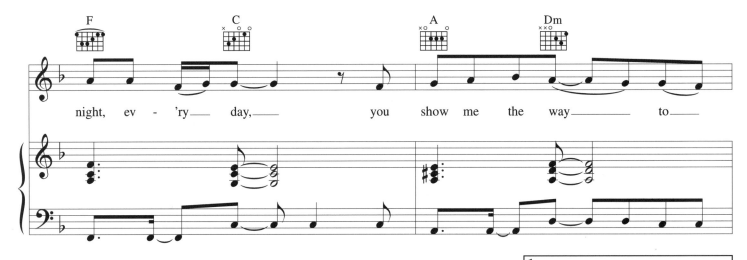

night, ev - 'ry— day,— you show me the way— to—

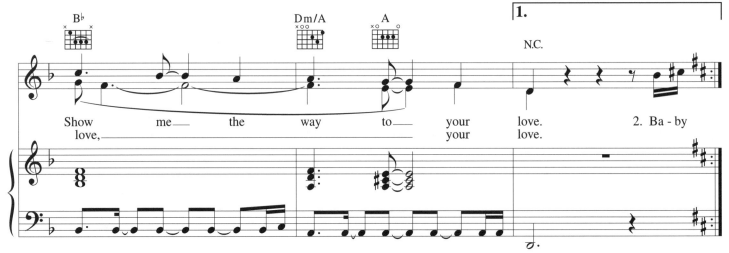

1.

Show me— the way to— your love.   2. Ba - by
love,—   your love.

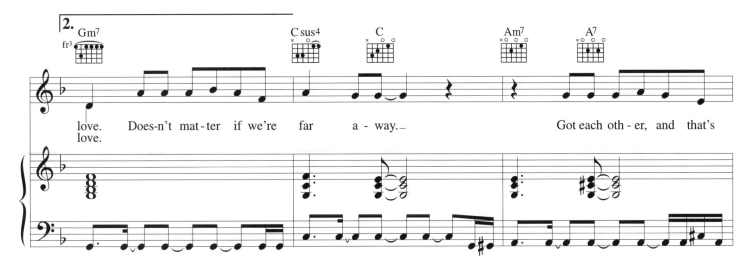

love. Does-n't mat-ter if we're far a - way.— Got each oth - er, and that's

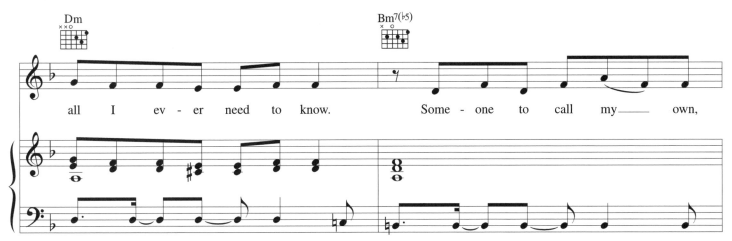

all I ev - er need to know. Some - one to call my—— own,

we'll be to-geth-er fi - - nal-ly,—— We're meant—— to be.—— Oh,

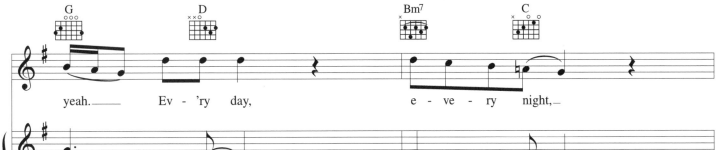

yeah.—— Ev - 'ry day, e - ve - ry night,—

fill my sha-dows, sha-dows with light.____ Ev-'ry night and

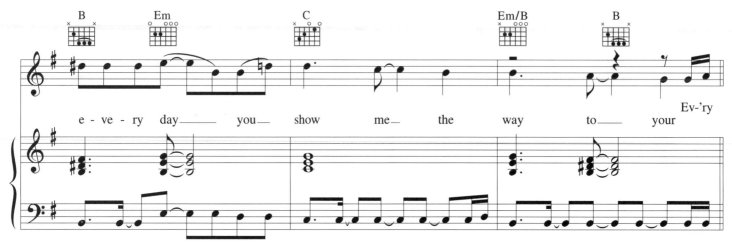

e-ve-ry day____ you show me__ the way to__ your Ev-'ry

day, ev-'ry__ night__ fill my sha-dows with light,__ When I
love.

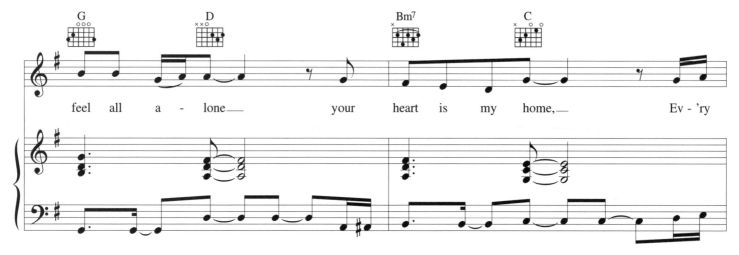

feel all a-lone__ your heart is my home,__ Ev-'ry

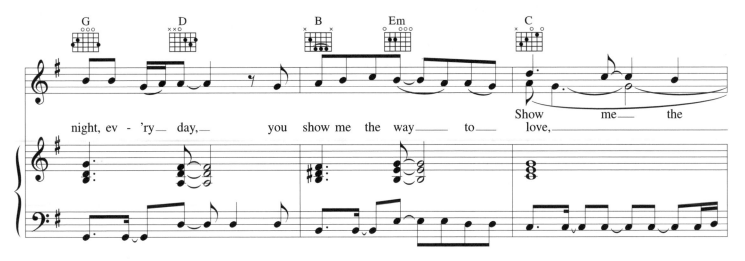

night, ev - 'ry — day, — you show me the way — to — love, Show me — the

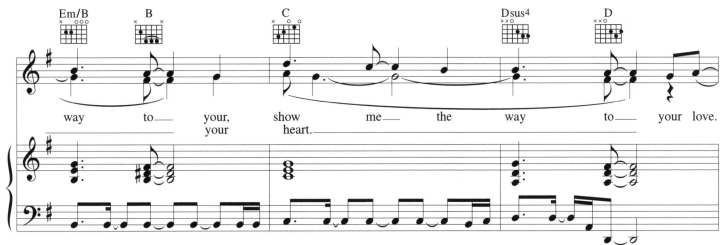

way to — your, show me — the way to — your love.
your heart. —

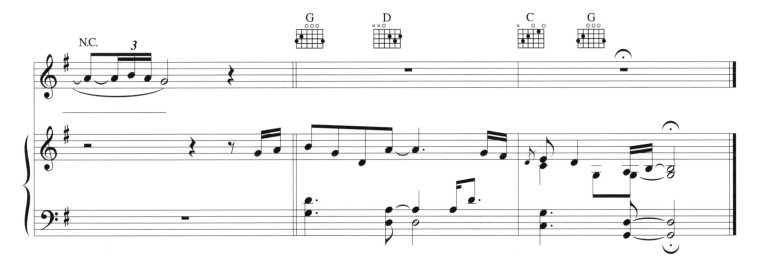

Verse 2:
Baby now that I've found you
Realize I was lost
Didn't know love could treat me this way
Maybe what it comes down to
When it matters the most
Is to find joy in every day.

We could sink to the bottom
We could climb to the top
'Cos together we'll never give up.

Every day, every night *etc.*

What Took You So Long?

Words & Music by Emma Bunton, Richard Stannard, Julian Gallagher, Martin Harrington, John Themis & Dave Morgan

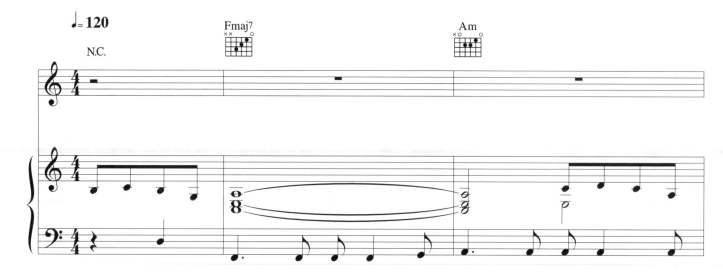

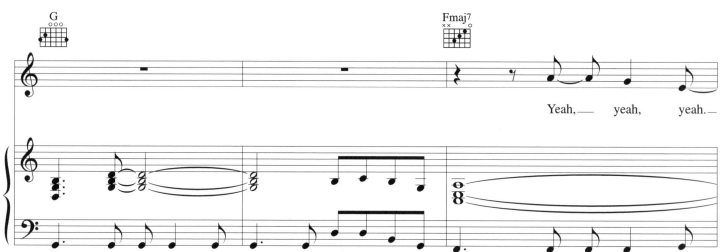

© Copyright 2001 EMI Music Publishing (WP) Limited, 127 Charing Cross Road, London WC2 (50%)/
Sony/ATV Music Publishing (UK) Limited, 10 Great Marlborough Street, London W1 (25%)/Biffco Music Publishing Limited/
Universal Music Publishing Limited, 77 Fulham Palace Road, London W6 (12.5%)/Copyright Control (12.5%).
All Rights Reserved. International Copyright Secured.

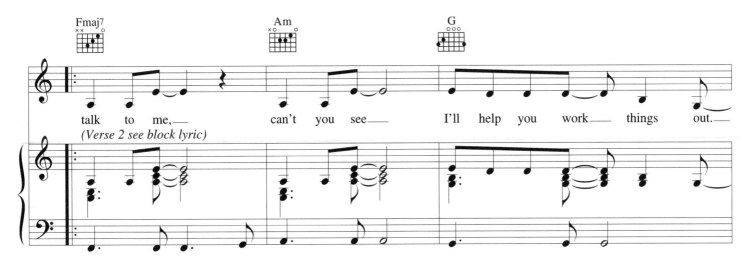

talk to me,— can't you see— I'll help you work— things out.—
(Verse 2 see block lyric)

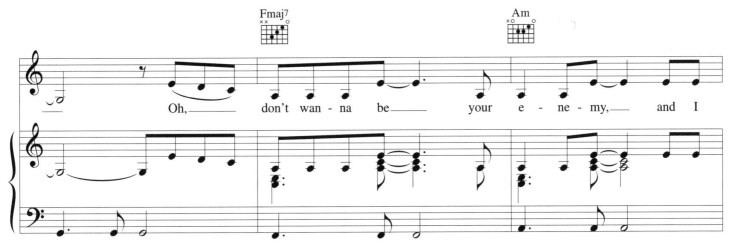

Oh,— don't wan - na be— your e - ne - my,— and I

don't wan - na scream— and— shout.— 'Cause ba - by I be - lieve— in hon-

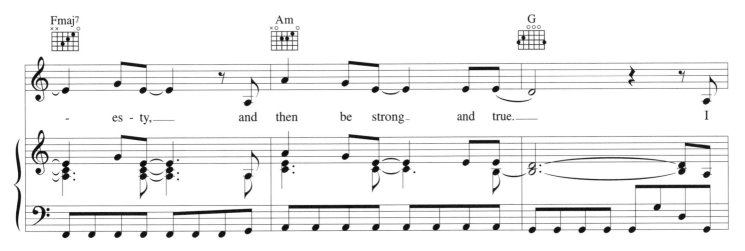

-es - ty,— and then be strong— and true.— I

should - n't have__ to say__ now ba - by, that I be - lieve__ in you.

__ What took you so long? What took you all

night? What took you for - ev – er to see__ I'm right? You know I treat you so

good, I make you feel fine. You know I'll nev - er give it up this time.

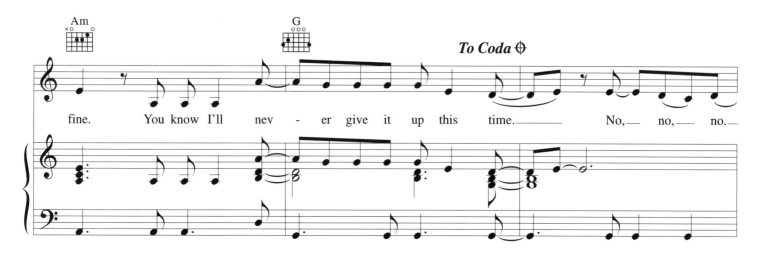

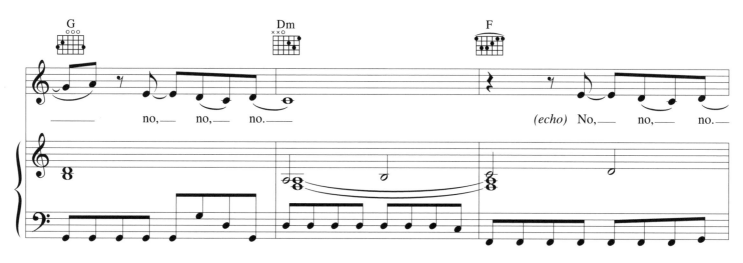

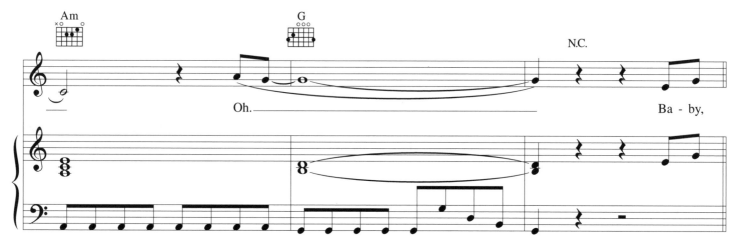

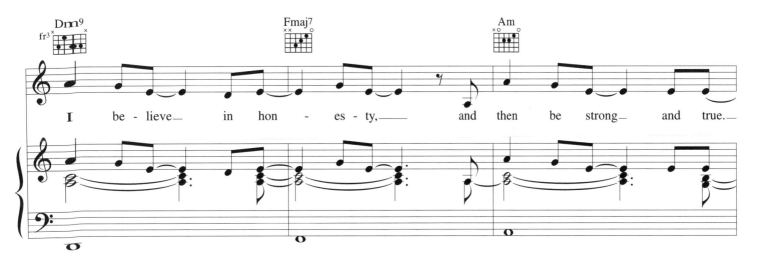

I be-lieve— in hon — es-ty,— and then be strong— and true.—

— I should-n't have— to say— now, ba — by, that

I be-lieve— in you.— What took you so

What took you so long? What took you all night? What took you for-ev-

Verse 2:
Oh, you touched my heart right from the start
You didn't know what to say
But honey I understand when you take my hand
Everything's okay
'Cause baby I believe reality
It's never far away
I've had enough, so listen baby
I've got something to say.

What took you so long *etc.*